# The Shoplifting Game

## Tana Reiff

A PACEMAKER **LifeTimes**™ BOOK

# LifeTimes™ Titles

So Long, Snowman
The Family from Vietnam
A Time to Choose
Mollie's Year
Juan and Lucy
A Place for Everyone
The Shoplifting Game

Editorial Director: Robert G. Bander
Managing Designer: Kauthar Hawkins
Cover, text design, and illustrations: Wayne Snyder
and Teresa Snyder

All characters herein are fictional. Any
resemblance to real persons is purely coincidental.

Library of Congress Catalog Card Number: 78-75222

ISBN 0-8224-4319-8
Printed in the United States of America
8 9 10 11 12    07 06 05 04 03

Globe
Fearon
Pearson Learning Group

**1-800-321-3106**
**www.pearsonlearning.com**

# Contents

# CHAPTER 1

It was
a busy winter Saturday.
The Mart store would be
full of people.
The clerks
would be busy.
What could be
a better time
to visit?

Beth had a job
in an office.
It was easy
but she didn't like it.
It didn't pay well, either.
Sometimes she didn't have
enough money
for things she wanted.
She wanted special clothes
to go
disco dancing in.

She wanted dresses
and lots of
new shoes.
She wanted records
and a color TV.
So she got very good
at shoplifting.

Beth went shoplifting
with her friends, Marty and Pam.
They always tried to see
who could come home
with the most stuff.
They started with small things:
rings, make-up, pins.
Then they tried
to steal small things
with high prices.
Soon they got tired of that.
So they worked on bigger things,
like clothes and radios.

Lots of the big stuff
they took
could be sold.
Marty's friend Tim,

would buy
small TVs and radios
from them.

"Look me up
anytime you want
to sell something
that plugs in,"
Tim said.

When Beth went
shoplifting with her friends,
Marty always took the most.
But she wasn't really
as good as Beth.
Pam was good, too.
But she got afraid
too fast.
She would start to laugh
when she took something
really good.
The three young women
had a pretty big business
until Marty got caught.
She got a heavy fine
and all kinds of problems.

That was enough
to stop Pam
from ever stealing again.

But Beth couldn't stop.
She kept it up.
She didn't think
it was really stealing.
It was getting even.
Prices were too high,
she thought.
Stores ripped off people,
so people
should rip off stores.
Fair is fair, she thought.

# Thinking It Over

1.  How do you feel about shoplifting?

2.  Do you go along with why Beth thinks shoplifting is OK?

3.  If you saw someone shoplifting, what would you do?

# CHAPTER 2

Beth drove her car
to the Mart.
She always drove
when she went shoplifting.
A clerk might see her
and start after her.
If she had a car,
the clerk could never
run fast enough
to catch her.

The trick was
to always keep your cool.
To look
like any other shopper.
Marty had given Beth
the idea
to buy something first.
Then she said
you could carry
the store's bag

and fill it
with other things.
But that's the way
Marty was caught,
Beth remembered.

That day, Marty went to
a big discount store
called Elco.
Right away she bought
a box of hair rollers.
Then she walked
to the back
of the store.
She picked up
a beautiful yellow sweater
and put it
in her Elco bag.
When she was almost
to the door,
a clerk came up to her.

The clerk asked her,
"Why are you still walking
around the store
with a bag?

You've already
bought something."

"I thought
of something else
I wanted to shop for,"
Marty said.

"I saw you buy
hair rollers,"
the clerk said.
"But it looks as if
your bag has
more than hair rollers
in it now."

The clerk called
the store manager.
The manager looked in
Marty's Elco bag
and found the sweater.
He called
the police.

After that happened,
her friends didn't see

Marty around
for a long time.
It was bad luck.
Things like that
don't often happen
in big discount stores.

Even after
Marty was caught
shoplifting,
Beth kept going to
stores like the Mart.
Why?
Because they didn't have
store detectives.
The store managers thought
you could always
pick out shoplifters.
Like an old lady
in a raincoat
on a sunny day
buying a Rolling Stones record.
But they were wrong.

The Mart had
no detectives

and very few clerks.
The clerks
were too busy
to look for shoplifters.
Most of them
really didn't care.

   Beth walked
through the Mart
looking at things.
Then she got
behind a clothes rack.
No one was looking.
She pulled a blouse
off the rack and
folded it
quick as could be.
She put it
into one of her big pockets.
Then she walked
out of the store.

# Thinking It Over

1.  What kind of store
    do you like best? Why?

2.  Is shoplifting
    like telling a lie?

3.  Can you often pick out
    a store detective?
    A shoplifter?

# CHAPTER 3

"I like your blouse,"
Skip said the next night.
"Is it new?"
Skip was Beth's boyfriend.

"Yes," said Beth.
"I got it yesterday."

"You must be
making a lot of money
at that office,"
said Skip.
"You're always getting
new clothes."

Skip knew nothing
about Beth's shoplifting.
He was a very honest guy.
Beth was afraid
he would break up with her
if he found out.

As long as she could
get away with it,
she would.

That night,
Beth and Skip
watched an old movie on TV.
Of all things,
it was about a woman
who always took things
from stores.
But in this movie
the woman could not
help herself.
The woman
had a real problem.
Beth began
to worry a little
as she watched the movie
with Skip.
She wondered,
Would he ever guess?

After the movie,
Skip said,
"Let's go get some food."

In the car
he said,
"I used to know a guy
who took stuff
from stores
all the time.
He said
he couldn't help it,
but everyone knew
that was just a line.
He finally got caught
and went to jail.
No one felt sorry
for him, either.
He asked for trouble
and he got it."

Beth sat back
in her seat.
She didn't say a word.

# Thinking It Over

1.  Can one lie
    lead to another?

2.  How is Skip's
    thinking different
    from Beth's?

3.  If you were a shoplifter,
    would you tell your friends?
    Why or why not?

# CHAPTER 4

The next day at work
was a drag for Beth.
She didn't want to go.
But she had to.
The office manager had said,
"One more day, Beth,
and I'm going to
have to let you go."
She wanted
to find another job.
But she was
too lazy to look.

Beth had never
thought of her shoplifting
as a problem.
Until the night before,
that is.
The movie
and what Skip had said
made her think.

Shoplifting was stealing.
It was against the law.
Maybe I'll stop it,
she thought.
And Skip—
if he ever found out,
he would leave me.
Is it worth that?
She thought about it
for a while.
Then she put it
out of her head
for the day.

The next day
was Thursday.
It was raining
when Beth woke up.
Again she didn't feel
like going to work.
But she did.
She was 10 minutes late.
No one called her down
about it.
They were just glad
to see her.

Things were slow that day.
There wasn't enough work
to keep everyone busy.
The office manager said
Beth could leave
at two o'clock.
That made her happy.

Beth left the office
and went
to her car.
But she didn't know
where to go.
It was too early
to go home.
She needed
something to do.

Of course,
she thought.
I'll go shopping.

# Thinking It Over

1.  For what reasons do
    people shoplift?

2.  Why is it hard
    for some people
    to stop doing things
    they know are bad for them?

## CHAPTER 5

Skip had asked Beth
to go dancing that night.
And Beth needed
a new top
to go with
her disco pants.

Something bright,
she thought.
Something people will
look at twice.
Something that will
catch the light.
Maybe satin.
Yes, that's it—
I'll get
a satin blouse.
I'll shop at Kelley's
for it.
It's the best department store
in town.

She drove
into Kelley's parking lot.
Then she walked
into the store.
Since it was
a Thursday afternoon,
the store
wasn't too crowded.

Beth walked
through the store.
She looked at
all kinds of things—
shirts, hats,
jars of make-up.
On one table
she found a rope belt
that she liked.
She bought it.
The clerk put the belt
in a bag
and handed the bag
to Beth.

When she came
to the blouse department,

Beth found
several other women
already there.
She walked away
until the shoppers
had gone
from the blouse racks.
Then she came back
and found the rack
where satin blouses
were hanging.

Beth started
to reach for
a yellow blouse.
Then something she saw
made her stop.

Across the room,
a young woman in jeans
was talking to a young man
wearing a backpack.
It didn't take long
for Beth to see
that the young woman was
a store detective.

She had caught
the young man
with a shoplifted shirt
in his backpack.
Beth watched the detective lead
the young man
to the front
of the store.

Beth's eyes opened wide.
This is Marty
all over again,
she thought.
I'd better
get out of here fast.
Real fast.

Climbing into her car,
she remembered
that bad things
often come in threes.
And I've seen
two bad things happen,
she thought.
What next?
Maybe it's that

I'll have to go
dancing tonight
in an old blouse.
I hope it's only that,
she thought.
I really do.


# Thinking It Over

1.   Do you ever see
     trouble coming?
     How?

2.   What makes people
     decide to act
     with more care?

# CHAPTER 6

After what happened
at Kelley's,
Beth tried
to stop shoplifting.
It worked
for two weeks.
Then she found
that she missed doing it
too much.
She wanted
to try
her luck
one more time.

The hardest stores
to steal clothes from
were little shops.
They had only one or two clerks
with nothing to do
but watch you.
It wasn't easy.

When Beth went with
Marty or Pam,
they would work together.
One would
keep the clerk busy
while another
would grab stuff.
But doing it alone
was hard,
and Beth knew it.

One day, Beth saw
a nice store called Mark's.
She went inside
to look at the new clothes.

The clerk asked,
"May I help you?"

"Just looking, thank you,"
said Beth.

Another woman
came into the store.
Beth was behind
a rack of pants.

The clerk spoke to
the new woman.
"Hello!
May I help you?"

"Yes, I need
a red blouse
to go with my black pants,"
said the woman.

"I have
just the right thing,"
said the clerk.
"Come over here."

Beth watched
the woman and the clerk
walk to the other side
of the shop.
The clerk
showed the woman
a rack of blouses.
Their backs
were turned
to Beth.
No one was watching her.

Beth looked down
at the rack of pants.
The green ones are great,
she thought.
They are my size, too.
She pulled them off the rack
and rolled them up.
She put them
in her big pocket.
Then she walked
out of Mark's.
It took no time at all.

I did it again,
she thought to herself.
It was too easy.
It was as if the pants
were asking me
to take them.

# Thinking It Over

1.  Have you ever done
    something that was
    "too easy"?

2.  Why would a person do
    something he or she
    didn't want to do?

3.  Did you ever
    "get away with" something?
    How did you feel?

# CHAPTER 7

Stealing that pair of pants
from Mark's
was no big thing
for Beth.
After a few days,
she almost forgot about it.

About a week
after Beth took the pants,
she was walking
down the street.
She was wearing
the green pants.
She saw Pam
and walked up to her.

"Hi, Pam,"
Beth said.
"How are you?
I haven't seen you
in a long time."

"I'm fine,"
said Pam.
"How are you?
How is your job?"

"I hate it,"
said Beth.
"I should quit.
I'm just too lazy
to look for another job."

"I know
what you mean,"
Pam said.

Beth didn't see
that they were standing
in front of Mark's.
But suddenly
a clerk ran
out of the store.

"You!
You, young lady!"
The clerk shouted
and pointed at Beth.

"I'll see you later, Beth,"
said Pam.
She walked away—fast.

The clerk took
Beth's arm.
"Don't try
to get away,"
she said.
"Come right into the shop.
There's someone
coming to see you."

Beth walked into Mark's
in front of the angry clerk.
They know me,
Beth thought.
Maybe they already
called the police.

A minute later
a cop walked into the store.
"Very nice pants
you have on, Miss,"
he said.
"Did you get them here?"

# Thinking It Over

1.  What would you do
    if you had a job
    you didn't like?

2.  Pam walked away
    from Beth very fast.
    What would you have done
    if you were Pam?

3.  If you were Beth,
    how would you answer
    the policeman's question?

# CHAPTER 8

The cop looked
right at Beth.
"We know
you have been pulling
this stuff
all over town.
But this is the first time
we could catch you
with some hot goods.
Now, did you
get those pants here?"

"No," Beth lied.
"I got them
at another place."

"Why don't you
tell that
to the chief
of police?
Come with me."

The cop made Beth
go with him
to the station.
He took her
to the chief of police.

"Hello, young lady,"
said the chief.
He read Beth her rights.
Then he asked Beth
where she got her pants.

Beth didn't know
what to say at first.
Then she said,
"OK, OK, I got them at Mark's."

The chief asked Beth
another question.
"Did you pay for them?"

Beth looked down.
She didn't say a word.

The chief spoke again.
"Did you pay for them?"

Beth looked up
at the chief
and said, "No."
That was all she said.
She was thinking
about what Skip would say
when he heard.
She knew
he'd never speak to her again.

"Shoplifting
is against the law."
The chief
looked at Beth.
"You will have to pay a fine.
Maybe as much as
a hundred dollars.
Maybe even some time
in jail.
The manager of Mark's shop
has no time for shoplifters."

Beth was trying
not to cry.
This had to happen
sometime.

She had known that.
Ever since Marty
was caught
at Elco's.
Ever since Beth had seen
the man get caught
at Kelley's.
Now she had to think
of a way out.

## Thinking It Over

1. Were the police
   too hard on Beth?
   Why or why not?

2. What do you do
   if someone pushes you
   to say something?

3. Is there a way out of
   everything if you think
   hard enough?
   Why or why not?

# CHAPTER 9

The chief spoke.
"Do you have
anything to say
before we book you
for shoplifting?"

"Yes," said Beth.
She looked at the chief.
She was frightened,
but she knew
she had to say something.
"You don't really know
that these pants
came from Mark's,"
Beth said.
"And you didn't see me
take them.
I can make
a telephone call
to someone, can't I?
Please let me make it."

   "Well, young lady,"
said the cop.
"Let me tell you something.
The manager of Mark's
is a very big man
in this town.
He wouldn't lie to us.
He says
your pants
came from his shop.
I feel we can
take his word for it."

   Beth still thought
it wasn't fair.
But she *had* taken the pants.
So what else could she say?
She called her lawyer.
Her lawyer's name
was Judith Reed.
Mrs. Reed had helped her once
when she got
a speeding ticket.

   She told Beth
not to say a word.

Of course,
Beth had talked already.
She had said that
she had not paid
for the pants.

Mrs. Reed came down
to the station.
She took care of everything
that had to be done
right away.
Beth might have to
go to court.
But that
would be later.
Thanks to Mrs. Reed,
Beth could go home now.
She didn't have to stay
at the police station.
Beth felt a little better.

"This is very interesting,"
Mrs. Reed told Beth.
"You see,
they didn't catch you
doing anything.

I don't think
they have a case."

Beth just hoped
Mrs. Reed was right.
She didn't know
what would
happen to her.

"I'll talk to you again
in a few days,"
Mrs. Reed said.
"There's something
I want to do
first."

# Thinking It Over

1. What are your rights
   if the police stop you?
   Why is it important
   to know your rights?

2. Do you think
   there are people
   who have power
   because they are rich?

3. If you were in trouble
   and you could make one call
   who would you call?

# CHAPTER 10

Judith Reed walked into
Mark's shop.
She had asked Mark Bell
if he could see her
that afternoon.
He had said yes.

When he saw
Judith come in
the shop
he held out
his hand to her.
They had known
each other
for several years.
They said hello
and smiled.

"Let's go into my office
to talk,"
he said.

When they sat down,
Mark Bell spoke.

"I'll bet I know
why you're here.
It's that
shoplifting case,
isn't it?"

"You're right, Mark,"
said Judith.
"I've come
to talk to you
right away
because I know
you're a man
of goodwill."

"And I know
that you
are a lawyer
with good sense,"
he said.

"Let's put
your goodwill

and my good sense
together," said Judith.
"Maybe we can
find a way
to work out this case.
A way that will help
*both* you
and the young woman."

"Let's try,"
said Mark Bell.
"Shoplifting helps no one.
I want to do
everything possible
to help people
understand this."

"There are
a number of ways
this case could go,"
said Judith.

"I know.
I could lose.
But I may be two jumps
ahead of you."

Judith looked
at Mark.
"How so?"

"I have asked myself
how this case
could be handled
so that it might not
happen again."

"Have you
come up with
any answers?"

"As a matter of fact,
I have," said Mark Bell.
"I'm very pleased
with one idea I've had.
So pleased
that I want to tell
the young woman *herself*
about it."

"Does that mean
that you want to see her?"
Judith hoped so.

"As soon as possible,"
Mark said.

Judith stood up.
"Thank you, Mark,"
she said.
"For whatever
you're going to do."

# Thinking It Over

1. Does going to jail
   help people learn
   right from wrong?

2. What kind of person
   is Mark Bell?

3. Is Judith Reed
   a good lawyer?
   Why or why not?

# CHAPTER 11

Judith Reed
called Beth the next day.
Beth was just about ready
to go home
from her office.

"I think
we can take care of your case
out of court,"
said Mrs. Reed.

Beth was surprised.
Then she said,
"What do you mean?"

"I want you
to talk to the manager
of Mark's shop.
Just be yourself.
Don't try
to fight with him.

Tell him
I told you to come.
I know him well.
He isn't a bad guy.
Try to look at it
this way.
Suppose you were he.
You run a little shop.
A woman walks out
with a pair of pants.
Lots of other people
have done the same thing.
How would you feel?"

   At that point
Beth felt very bad.
"I see what you mean,
Mrs. Reed.
I never thought of it
that way before."

   Judith Reed went on.
"You don't have a shop.
People can't steal from you
in that way.
But what if someone

came into your house
and took your TV set?
Or your chair?
Or anything you owned?
You wouldn't feel so good,
would you?"

"Not at all,"
Beth said.
She thought
of all the things
she had taken.
She wished
she had never started.
Maybe it was
too late now
to make things right
or maybe it wasn't.

Beth spoke again.
"Can I go talk to him now?"

"Yes,"
said Mrs. Reed.
"I told him
you would be there

about five o'clock.
He's waiting for you."

Beth wondered
what the manager
of Mark's
would say and do.
She knew
that saying
she was sorry
would not be enough.
But Mrs. Reed
could be trusted.
Beth knew that.
So she got ready
to go to Mark's.
She would see what
the manager would do.

# Thinking It Over

1.  How do you feel
    about what Judith Reed said
    about shoplifting?

2.  Does it matter
    that Judith Reed knows
    the store manager?
    Why or why not?
    *Should* it matter?

3.  How would you feel
    right now
    if you were Beth?

# CHAPTER 12

After work, Beth went
right to Mark's.
She was afraid
to talk to the man.
But she knew
she had to.
She felt she was wrong.
She even felt sorry.
But what could she say to him?
Would he be very angry?

He said his name
was Mark Bell.
He seemed very nice.
He started to talk.

"I'm glad
you came down here,"
he said.
"This makes things
better for both of us.

Let me give you
my side of the story.
I don't like shoplifting.
No store manager does.
But let me tell you something.
When people steal
from my store,
I get hurt.
But the people
who buy from me
get hurt more.
They get hurt
because I must
raise prices
to make up
for what I lost.
Can you see this?"

"Yes," said Beth.
"I do.
But I never thought about it.
I guess
if people would stop stealing
from stores,
it would help
keep prices down."

"It would help,"
said Mark Bell.
"When you steal
from my store,
everyone else
pays for what you take."

"That means
I'm hurting
my own friends,"
Beth said.
"A lot of my friends
shop here."
She felt
even worse than before.

"You're a nice young woman,"
said Mark.
"I'm glad you know
you're wrong.
But you have to stop
these tricks.
It's just no good."

Beth had learned
her lesson.

She was sure of that.
She told Mark Bell.
"I guess I must pay a fine
and all that.
But I don't know
how I can.
Please don't send me to jail."

Mark smiled.
"I think
we can work something out."

# Thinking It Over

1.  Does what Mark said to Beth
    make sense to you?

2.  What are some other things
    that make prices go up?
    Go down?

3.  If you were Mark Bell,
    how would you want Beth
    to pay for her stealing?

# CHAPTER 13

I'm pretty lucky,
thought Beth.
I took a pair of pants
from Mark's.
That was against the law.
And now here I am
working at Mark's.

Mark Bell and Beth
had worked out
a great plan.
They had decided that
Beth would quit her office job,
and go to work
at Mark's.

The plan was
that she would not get paid
for the first week.
That would take care
of the fine.

If she did well
that first week,
Mark would keep her on
as a sales clerk.
Then she would get paid
for her work.
She would have
a great new job.

Mark Bell wanted Beth
to see what it was like
to work in a store.
She would be
on the other side now.
She would see for herself
why shoplifting
is a problem.

From the
very first day,
Beth liked her new job.
She told Skip everything,
and he still took her out.
For Beth,
the shoplifting game
was over.

All over.
And she felt like
the winner.

# Thinking It Over

1.  Do you think Mark's plan
    for Beth was fair?
    Why or why not?
    Should someone like Beth
    go to jail instead?

2.  Some people say:
    "A friend is someone
    who knows all about you
    and still likes you."
    What do you think?

3.  How would you now answer
    the question
    "How do you feel
    about shoplifting?"
    Would you answer
    the same as you did
    after reading Chapter 1?